Lucy Rowland  Katy Halford

There's No Such Thing As...
UNICORNS

FARM

ZOO

LAKE

WOOD

MEADOW

BEACH + CAVE

SCHOOL

PARK

SCHOLASTIC

"There's **no such thing** as unicorns,"

my brother said last night.

Today I'll go **exploring**

just to see if he is right.

I've packed my **map, binoculars**

. . . there's **such** a lot to do!

And so much **searching** to be done so **could YOU** help me too?

There's **no such thing** as unicorns.
The **farmer** told me so.

She has **a lot** of animals.

I guess that she would know.

There's **no such thing** as unicorns.

I've searched around the ZOO.

PENGUINS
• AFRICAN, NAMIBIA
• CURRENT POPULAT
  50,000
• ENDANGERED
• DIET: KRILL, SQ

TROPICAL BIRDS

GiRAFFES
- TALLEST MAMMAL
- THREE HEARTS
- A NEWBORN GIRAFFE IS SIX FEET TALL
- DIET: LEAVES, TWIGS AND BARK

They **must** be somewhere hiding

as they've disappeared from view.

There's **no such thing** as unicorns.
I hunted round the **lake.**

I thought I saw one in the trees?

It must be a mistake.

There's **no such thing** as unicorns.

I checked inside the wood.

And if they're playing 'Hide and Seek'

they're really **very** good!

There's **no such thing** as **unicorns**.

The **meadow** was quite bare.

I saw some wild ponies

but **no unicorns** were there.

There's **no such thing** as unicorns.

The beach had **one fat seal,**

three **crabs,**

some **shells,**

a **starfish.**

Maybe unicorns **aren't** real.

There's **no such thing** as unicorns.

Next, trying to be **brave**,

I turned my torch on carefully . . .

Nope!

None inside the cave!

"There's **no such thing** as unicorns,"

my teacher said to me.

I hunted round the **classroom**

there were **none** that I could see.

There's **no such thing** as unicorns.

I even tried the **park**.

I searched around the slide and swings

until it grew quite dark.

"Oh, **there** you are!" my brother calls,

"I've looked all round for you!"

"There's **no such thing** as unicorns," I sob.

"It must be TRUE."

He **cuddles** me up gently and
he tells me it's all right.

We make a wish upon a star
that's shining through the night.

Then, on our way back home again . . .

a sparkle in the air . . .

a silver light begins to shine . . .

A UNICORN!

Right there!

My brother blinks. He rubs his eyes,

he thinks we've got it wrong.

BUT....there ARE such things as unicorns!

I knew it all along.

First published in 2021 by Scholastic Children's Books
a division of Scholastic Ltd
Euston House, 24 Eversholt Street
London NW1 1DB

www.scholastic.co.uk

London – New York – Toronto – Sydney – Auckland
Mexico City – New Delhi – Hong Kong

PB ISBN 978 0702 30068 4
C&F ISBN 978 0702 30614 3